SRA
Open Court Reading

We See a Tree

A Division of The McGraw·Hill Companies

Columbus, Ohio

SRA/McGraw-Hill

A Division of The **McGraw·Hill** *Companies*

Send all inquiries to:
SRA/McGraw-Hill
8787 Orion Place
Columbus, Ohio 43240-4027

ISBN 0-02-660806-5
2 3 4 5 6 7 8 9 DBH 04 03 02 01 00

We see a .

tree

We see a .

tree

We see   .

green   leaves

4

We see a .

tree

3

We see a .

tree

We see green .

leaves

4

We see a .

tree

We see   and 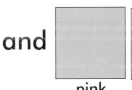 .

green leaves   pink flowers

5

We see a .

tree

We see green  and green .

green leaves green apples

6

We see a .

tree

We see and .

green leaves   red apples

7

My  see.

eyes

My  see.

hands

8